ISBN 0-85116-575-3

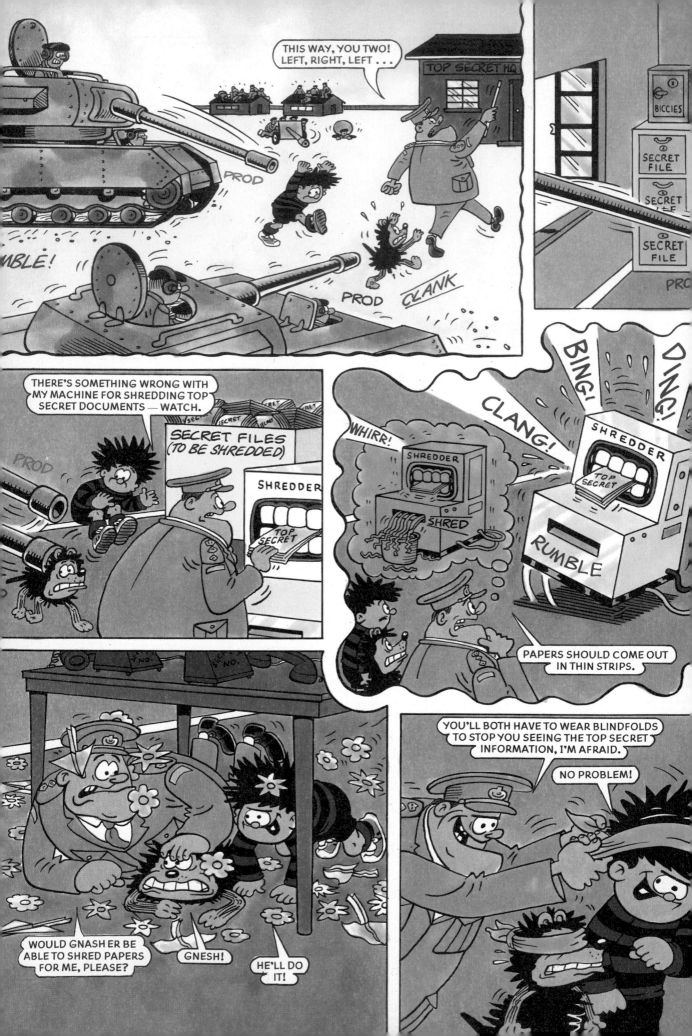

CRAZY CREATURE FEATURE
Starring – SIDNEY from The BASH St. KID'S ODD PETS

THE HIPPOPOTAMOTH

Don't ask me cos I don't know why
The *Hippopotamoth* can fly.
It is one of life's strangest things,
How it takes off with these frail wings.

A normal moth may chew small holes
In jerseys, shirts or coats or stoles.
But you should see how this brute eats —
It guzzles down whole quilts and sheets!

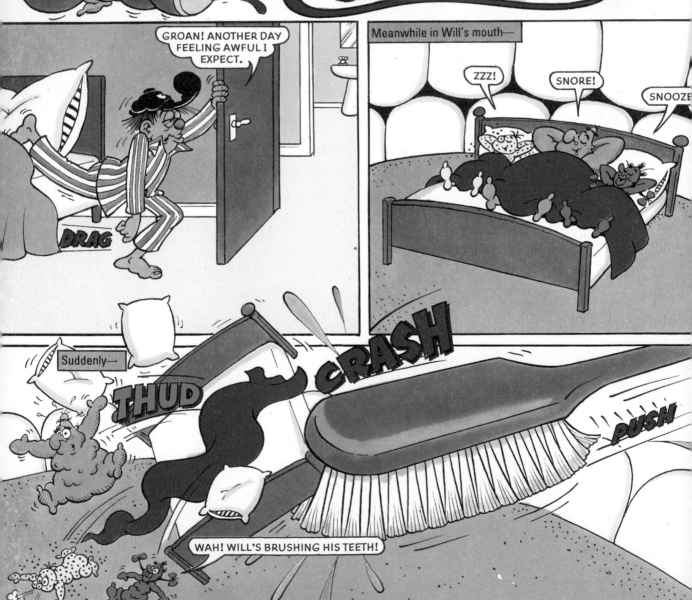

ROGER THE DODGER

Then —

YOWL!

WHAT'S GOING ON?

SO! A TRAINED MOUSE. WHAT A SNEAKY DODGE!

HEH-HEH! GOT REVENGE ON THAT CAT!

YOU CHEAT!

YERK!

GASP! ESCAPED. WHERE IS THAT BLOOMIN' MOUSE?

FORGOTTEN HEROES

SCRATCH

HAVE YOU DONE YOUR PROJECTS ABOUT FAMOUS PEOPLE IN HISTORY?

OF COURSE!

FROWN

HERE IT IS! I'VE WRITTEN ABOUT THE EGYPTIAN KING TUTANKAMEN!

DISGUSTED

THANK YOU, CUTHBERT.

CUTHBERT

DUST

GOODNESS, CUTHBERT! YOUR HANDWRITING IS SHOCKING!

DELIGHTED

FROWN

CUTHBERT

I'VE WRITTEN THE WHOLE THING IN HIEROGLYPHICS. SMARM!

OH!

AHEM! I'LL READ IT LATER THEN!

MIFFED

TEACHER'S DESK

And—

PUSH

WE'VE DONE A JOINT PROJECT, TEACHER — LET US SHOW IT TO YOU!

VERY WELL!

KIDS' PROJECT

LIFT

Turn the page to see what the Kids have done!

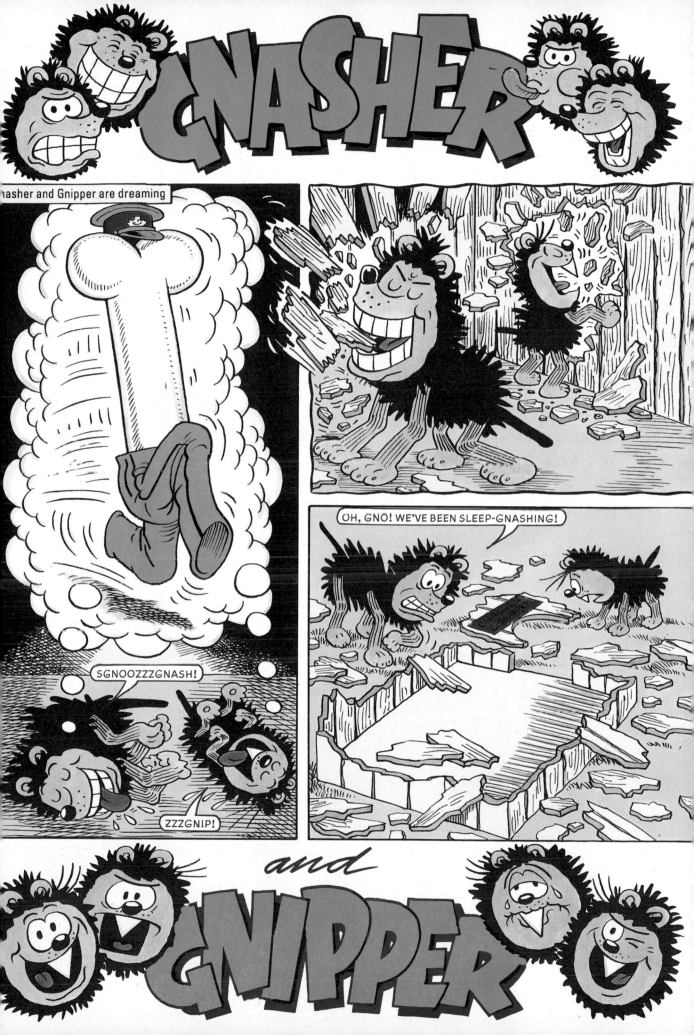

WE'LL HAVE TO FIND A NEW PLACE TO SLEEP.

HERE'S A NICE, METAL KENNEL FOR US TO SLEEP IN.

GNO, GNIPPER!

LIFT

TOPPLE RUMBLE

THAT'S THE COAL BUNKER!

Soon —

WE COULD STAY IN THIS WATER PIPE.

Alas —

GNEH?

CLICK

CLICK

PLAN

THAT'S THE NEW WATER SUPPLY CONNECTED.

Back home —

TIME TO WASH THE DISHES.

TURN

WHAT'S GOING ON?

POP

POP

GASP!

THANK GOODNESS WE'RE OUT OF THERE.

CLUMP

THUD

Shortly —

HOTEL REAR ENTRANCE

THE VERY THING!

WAHEY!

GREAT FOR CHASING CATS, TOO!

MEOWK!

SCREECH!

RUMBLE

FLATTEN

FLATTEN

ONE SMALL PROBLEM . . .

RUMBLE

HMM! NO CLUES AS TO HOW THIS WAS BUILT!

Suddenly—

YIKES!

CRASH!

WOW! AN ANCIENT BUILDER'S OFFICE BELOW THE PYRAMID! I SHOULD FIND THE ANSWER DOWN HERE!

D.I.Y. PYRAMID BUILDING

PLANS

Sure enough—

AHA! NOW I KNOW!

D.I.Y. PYRAMID BUILDING.

So—

HOME

I'LL TAKE A FEW BLOCKS BACK TO SCHOOL TO DEMONSTRATE!

Back at school—

LEFT A BIT . . .

SPECIAL OFFER ON SATELLITE TV!

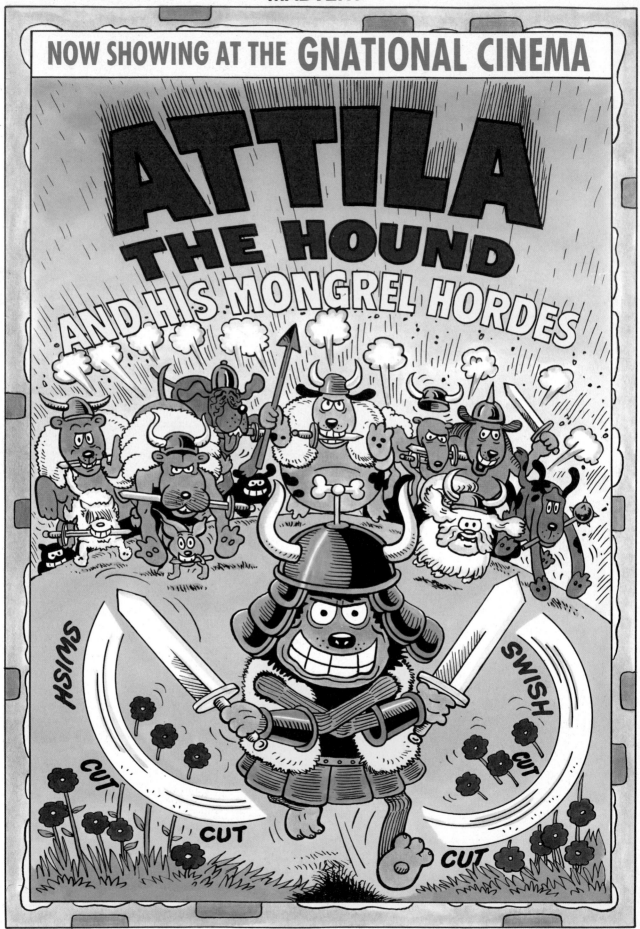

General Jumbo
JUMBO JOHNSON, the Dinchester schoolboy who commanded his very own private army of super radio controlled models, had heard that an elderly friend was sick. So that Saturday morning . . .
HI, MR BRENNAN. I'VE BROUGHT SOME SUPPLIES.
WOW! THANKS, JUMBO -- COUGH! — I FEEL BETTER ALREADY.

Just then, Professor Carter, the inventor of Jumbo's wonderful models, arrived . . .

I THINK YOU'VE FORGOTTEN SOMETHING, JUMBO.

WHAT'S THAT, PROF?

YOU PROMISED TO HELP ME PAINT MY HOUSE TODAY.

So, presently—

HMPH! DON'T WORK TOO HARD, JUMBO.

MANY MODELS MAKE LIGHT WORK, PROF.

Just then—

H-HEY!

LOOK O

THESE COPTERS WILL CLEAN YOUR BRICKWORK.

From his high vantage point, Jumbo had a good view of the surrounding area . . .

HELLO! WHAT'S GOING ON IN THAT CAR PARK?

At the Professor's house—

Jumbo used his remote-control gadget to call up two helicopters . . .

NOW TO DEAL WITH SOME OF THE HIGHER PLACES.

THIEVES — STEALING FROM THE VEHICLES IN THE CAR PARK!

Jumbo's fingers flitted over the buttons on his remote-control gadget . . .

GOT TO STOP THIS.

The General sent the paint carrying copters on a mission . . .

Jumbo sent miniature missiles soaring upwards . . .

. . . then ropes with grappling hooks were fired.

HE'S ONLY A STUPID KID.

OUT OF OUR WAY!

In the nick of time, Jumbo's army arrived.

LET'S GO!

Just then, the roar of a powerful engine was heard . . .

OH-OH! WHO'S COMING?

ROAR!

OUR BOSS — THAT'S WHO!

I'LL FIX YOU, YOU INTERFERING BRAT.

HE MEANS BUSINESS!

The tyre burst sending the car out of control . . .

WHEW! IT WORKED!

FUEL LEAKING — THAT'S A FIRE HAZARD.

Powerful magnets and grappling hooks stuck to the door . . .

NOW . . . ALTOGETHER . . .

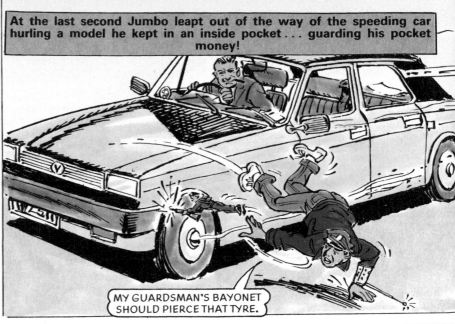

At the last second Jumbo leapt out of the way of the speeding car hurling a model he kept in an inside pocket . . . guarding his pocket money!

I'VE SOMETHING IN MY POCKET TO FIX HIM.

MY GUARDSMAN'S BAYONET SHOULD PIERCE THAT TYRE.

Swiftly, Jumbo summoned all his models . . .

HE'S KNOCKED OUT. GOT TO GET HIM OUT OF THE CAR, BUT THE DOOR'S JAMMED!

. . . PULL!

At that moment, the police arrived . . .

OH! MY HEAD!

Within minutes the ambulance and fire brigade had arrived.

HOW DID YOU GET HERE SO QUICKLY? I DIDN'T HAVE TIME TO PHONE YOU.

IT WAS EASY. WE HAD COMPLAINTS ABOUT A PAINT TRAIL . . . AND JUST FOLLOWED THAT.

Outside—

JUST AS WELL I INVENTED A SUPER PAINT REMOVER, EH, JUMBO?

So it was 'fatigues' for Jumbo and his army . . .

CHEER UP, JUMBO. YOUR ORDERS ARE THROUGH FROM THE CAR PARK OWNER. YOU'VE BEEN POSTED TO A BEACH IN SPAIN FOR TWO WEEKS.

CRAZY CREATURE FEATURE
Starring – SIDNEY from The BASH St. KID'S ODD PETS

THE ELEPHANTELOPE

I own an *Elephantelope* —
A huge but sprightly creature.
She might do clever tricks I hope,
If I can only teach 'er.

A dainty leap, a pirouette —
I think I'll try some more.
Oh, goodness! How could I forget,
We're on the seventh floor!

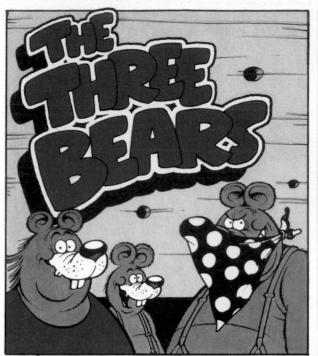

In Hank's Store —

LES PRETEND

visits

EH! I'LL SUCK UP S OXTAIL SOUP . .

. . . AND FILL THE BALL WITH IT!

OPS! IT'S GONE OVER THE WALL OF THAT STRANGE HOUSE!

AH! THERE IT IS IN THAT SUPER MUCKY SWAMP!

YUM! THIS LOOKS TASTY!

EH?

A SOUP-CENTRED GOBSTOPPER! DELICIOUS!

G-G-GASP!

BEST DRESSED PESTS

MEMPHIS MENACE

GNUWK GNOCKER

HOUNDDAWG

THESE FLARES ARE GREAT FOR HIDING GNASHER UNDER. NOT SO KEEN ON PEACE AND LOVE, THOUGH!
MELLOW MENACE
OW-OW-EEK!
SPLAT
SPLAT
LIFT
PHUT!
GRUNGY GNASHER

"SHOW MIN THE WAY TO GO HOME!"

WHERE WILL MINNIE END UP?

FIND OUT IN A COUPLE OF PAGES

WE LEFT MIN IN A WARDROBE—LET'S SEE HOW SHE'S GETTING ON!

THOSE PEOPLE HAVEN'T FOUND ME — SHOULD BE SAFE TO COME OUT!

WHERE AM I?

GASP! I'M IN A FURNITURE VAN!

EVEN WORSE — I'M ON A BOAT!

MUST GET BACK TO BRITAIN!

So —

GERONIMO!

MIND YOU! I THINK YOU COULD TELL WITHOUT THE STICKER. CHUCKLE!

Dennis was here!

BASH STREET KIDZ ROOL!

So —

THIS MUST BE THE LANE THAT TAILS BACK TO BEANOTOWN.

I SAY!

PARP!

YOU SAY WHAT?

PARP!

A LORRY NEXT.

HMM! LOOKS LIKE I'LL HAVE TO SWIM ACROSS THIS!

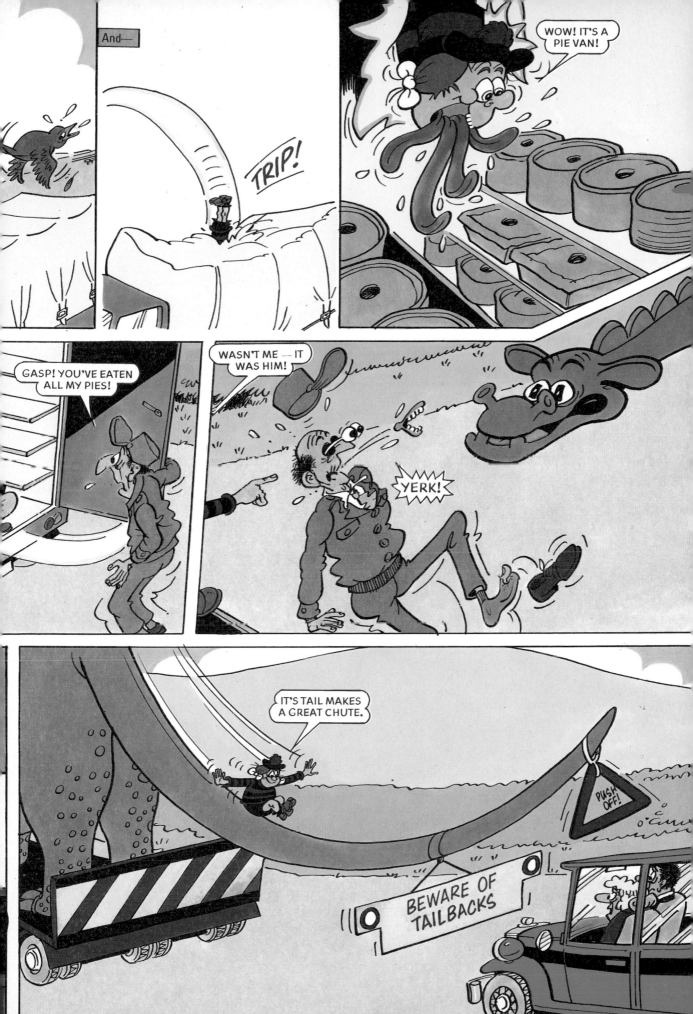

THAT WON'T STOP MA BEAR.

HOI! THAT'S OUR LUNCH!

CRISPS

I'LL SOON BE DINING IN STYLE.

I'M ALMOST READY!

TAP! TAP!

I'M ON MY WAY!

CLANG!

'MORNING, HANK!

'MORNING, DUSTBIN!

IT'S YOU, MA BEAR! PREPARE TO BE PEPPERED!

BUNG!

BEST BANGERS

SCOOP!

SWIPE!

BOING!

BLAM!

TAKE THAT — YAROO!

HAW-HAW! LOOKS LIKE I WIN, HANK. CHOMP!

PITY YOU RAIDED ME ON A MONDAY, MA.

MUNCH! CHOMP!

EH? WHY?

COS MONDAYS THE DAY THE BINS ARE EMPTIED!

WAAA!

HEAVE

GREEDY GULCH RUBBISH CART

Soon —

LOOK! LUCKY MA'S HAVIN' HERSELF A FEAST.

SPLUTTER!

RUBBISH

BAH! I CAN'T GET TO SLEEP!

HEY! I COULD COUNT THE NUMBER OF GOALS I SCORED TODAY INSTEAD OF SHEEP!

HUH! I DIDN'T SCORE ANY GOALS TODAY, THOUGH!

So—

I'LL WATCH A VIDEO.

And—

THIS OLD GAME IS A CRACKER!

CRAZY CREATURE FEATURE
Starring – SIDNEY from The BASH St. KID'S ODD PETS

THE PELICANARY

I've got a pet *Pelicanary,*
Which sings like that bloke Pavarotti.
Its voice is so good that it's scary —
Though it cheats, which is terribly naughty.

It has a huge mouth like a dustbin,
Designed to store grub that he gets.
But look what the rascal has thrust in —
A machine playing music cassettes!

SWOON!

SNIFF! I'LL PICK ONE OF THESE FLOWERS TO PRESS SINCE THERE ARE PLENTY!

SNIFF
SNIFF

SWISH
SWISH
SWISH

WHAT ARE YOU DOING, SMIFFY?

HO-HO! LOTS OF PRESSED FLOWERS NOW!

DOH!

OH, NO! SMIFFY'S CRACKED ONE OF BEANOTOWN'S ANCIENT LANDMARKS!

SEE IF WE CA PUSH IT TOGETH AND GLUE IT

HOI! WHO ARE YOU CALLING A BOY? I'M AT LEAST 6,000 YEARS OLD!

EH? SORRY!

SIR! SIR! LOOK WHAT WAS INSIDE THAT ROCK — A STONE AGE BOY . . . ER . . . MAN!

CAN HE JOIN OUR CLASS?

WOW! FIND OF THE CENTURY — YES! BACK TO SCHOOL, KIDS!

CLASS II B

NNNGH!

OW!

BOYLP!

I'M COLLECTING AIR TO PUT IN MY JAR, DANNY!

VISH

HO-HO! SILLY FELLOW!

OOF!

BOUNCE

TRIP

CRACK

EEEK!

ANCIENT STAND...

HOI! YOU'RE SQUASHING ME!

GASP! WHO SAID THAT?

PUSH

PUSH

ANCIENT STA...

PHEW! I'VE BEEN TRAPPED IN THERE FOR YEARS!

G...GASP! A STONE AGE BOY!

ANCIENT

NOTHING EVER CHANGES! I CAN BIT OF CAVE WALL PAINTING, TOO!

E MY UEST!

$1 + 1 = 2$
$2 + 2 = 4$
$3 + 3 = 6$
$4 + 4 = 8$

$7 - 1 = 6$
$9 - 3 = 6$
$12 - 6 = 6$

WONDERFUL!

HA-HA!

COO!

GREAT!

JUDGE FOR YOURSELF THE BEST OF THESE SIX JOKES. TURN THE PAGE TO SEE IF YOU AGREE WITH OUR CELEBRITY EXPERT . . . BUT FIRST PUT ON A RAINCOAT!!

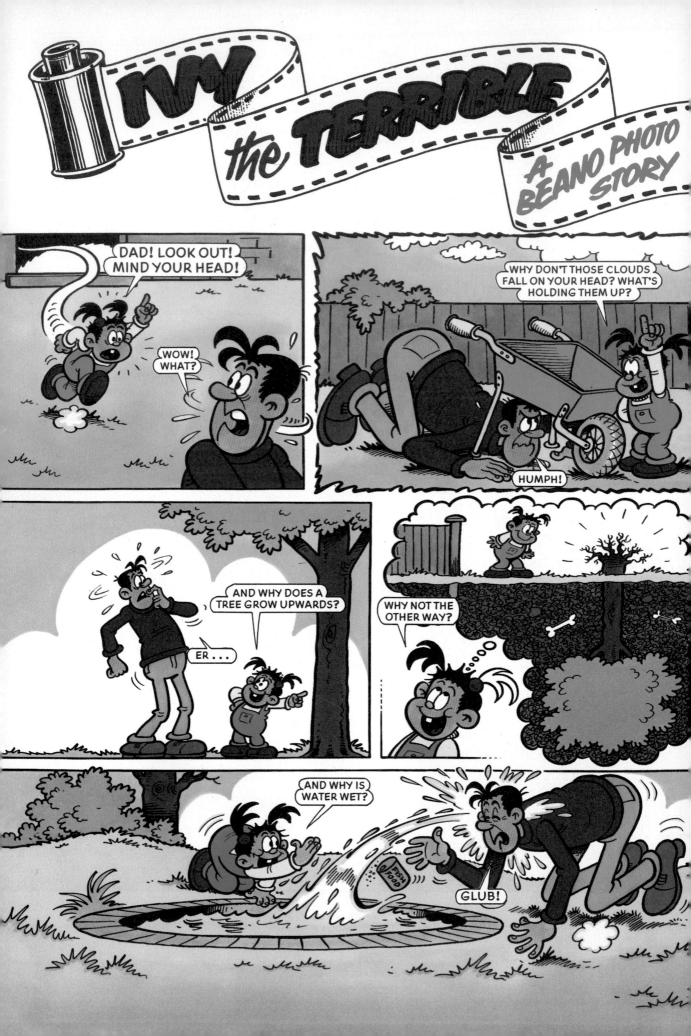

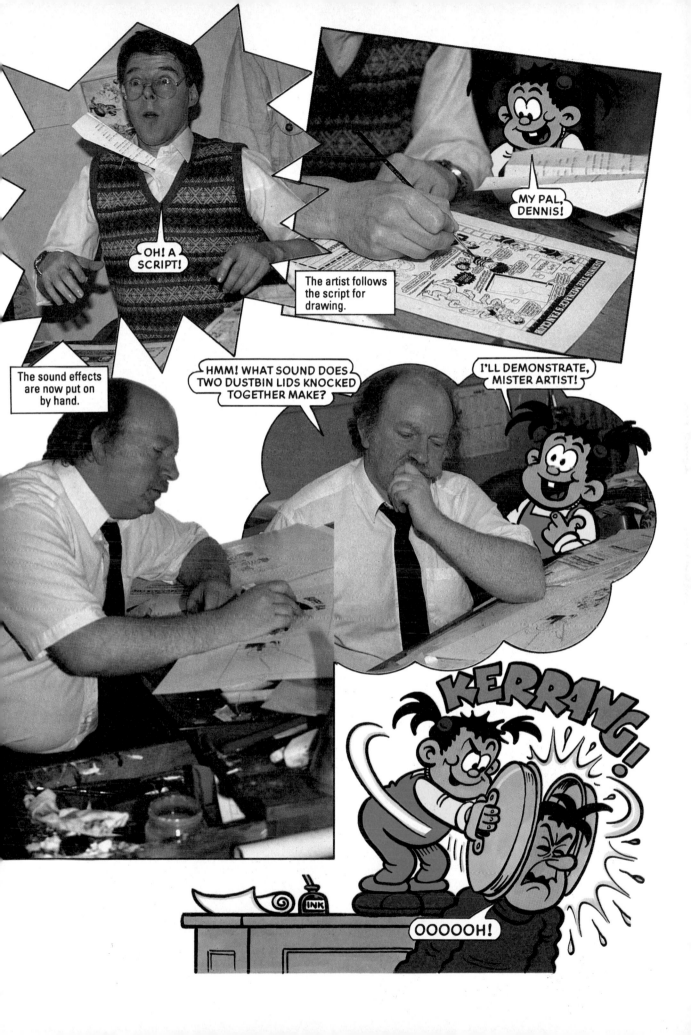

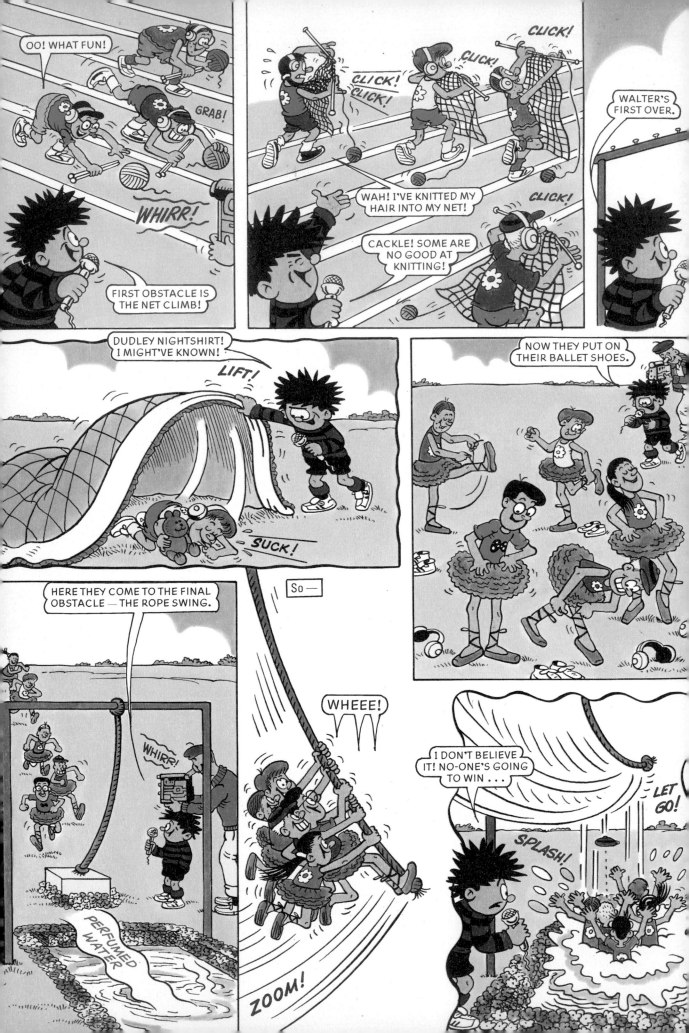

CRAZY CREATURE FEATURE
Starring – SIDNEY from The BASH St. KID'S ODD PETS

THE BUFFALOCTOPUS

The *Buffaloctopus* abides,
In rock holes beneath the tides.
A frightful denizen of the seas,
It has webbed feet and knobbly knees.

Among the coral see him sitting,
His eight legs are busy knitting
A shell suit, in a shade quite pale,
For his best mate the Killer Whale.

GRAN GO

DANNY'S NANNY